Librarian Reviewer
Diane R. Chen

Reading Consultant
Mark DeYoung

www.raintreepublishers.co.uk
Visit our website to find out more information about Raintree books.

To order:
Phone 0845 6044371
Fax +44 (0) 1865 312263
Email myorders@raintreepublishers.co.uk

Customers from outside the UK please telephone +44 1865 312262

Raintree is an imprint of Capstone Global Library Limited, a company incorporated in England and Wales having its registered office at 7 Pilgrim Street, London, EC4V 6LB – Registered company number: 6695582

First published in hardback and paperback in the United Kingdom by Capstone Global Library in 2010

Art Director: Heather Kindseth
Designer: Keegan Gilbert
Editor: Vaarunika Dharmapala
Originated by Capstone Global Library Ltd
Printed and bound in China by Leo Paper Products Ltd

ISBN 978 1 406216 61 5 (hardback)
14 13 12 11 10
10 9 8 7 6 5 4 3 2 1

ISBN 978 1 406216 64 6 (paperback)
14 13 12 11 10
10 9 8 7 6 5 4 3 2 1

British Library Cataloguing in Publication Data
A full catalogue record for this book is available from the British Library.

BY AARON REYNOLDS
ILLUSTRATED BY ERIK LERVOLD

Cast of CHARACTERS

DIRT
Sluggo
ENGLISH
MATHS
Mrs Mandible
Fruit Fly Boys

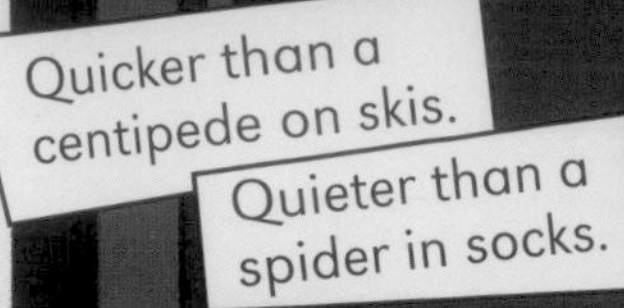

More lethal than a stink bug's breath.

I am Tiger Moth, Insect Ninja.

Harnessing the ancient powers of martial arts for good, I strike fear into the hearts of all criminal insects. Well, in Year Five, anyway.

Monday afternoon. Antennae Primary School.

There was a horrible crime I couldn't work out: why do teachers make kids do school plays, anyway?

Tiger, I told you to take the painting off the wall and then say your line.

Yes, Mrs Mandible. Sorry.

And be careful with that painting, Tiger. It's very delicate.

And Tiger, you must remember your lines. Sluggo and Flutter already have theirs memorized.
Yes, Mrs Mandible.
Good job today, Sluggo and Flutter.
Thank you, Mrs Mandible.
As if play practice weren't painful enough . . .
Wow, Tiger, that was great acting!
I think you might be up for a Cricket's Choice award.
I'm a ninja, not an actor. N-I-N-J-A.
. . . I had to put up with put-downs from my apprentice, Kung Pow.
Oh, Kung Pow, be very careful with that painting.
It's worth a great deal.
Yes, Mrs Mandible.

Come on, help me put these props away.
PROPS
Next time, I get to be props bug and **you** can be in Pest Side Story.
Over my cold exoskeleton.
That can be arranged more easily than you know.
It was the Fruit Fly Boys.
What are you doing in the props cupboard?
Propping stuff up.
Yeah, propping stuff up. Good one.
What a couple of parasites.
I should have suspected trouble straight away. Those two maggots had a habit of burrowing into unsavoury situations.

The next day at lunch.
I was just finishing my dung dumplings when Mrs Mandible barged into the cafeteria.
It's gone! The painting is gone!
Kung Pow, I told you to be careful with that painting for the play! Where is it?
It's in the props cupboard. I saw him put it there myself.

An original Leonardo DeLacewing! It's one of his early versions of the Mona Larva.
That isn't just another prop, Kung Pow. That painting is a valuable antique.
Then why are we using it for the play?
I thought it would give the play a touch of authenticity.
If it doesn't turn up, I don't know what we'll do!

That's just great! I'm props bug. Guess who's going to get the blame for this!
Not if I can help it. Don't forget who you're eating lunch with.
Tiger Moth, Insect Ninja.
What are you going to do?
Watch and learn, woodworm.
Woodlouse. I'm a woodlouse.
Whatever.

Ninja work isn't all kung fu and flying over rooftops. It was time to put my brain into action. I had to dig my way to the slimy bottom of this puzzle.

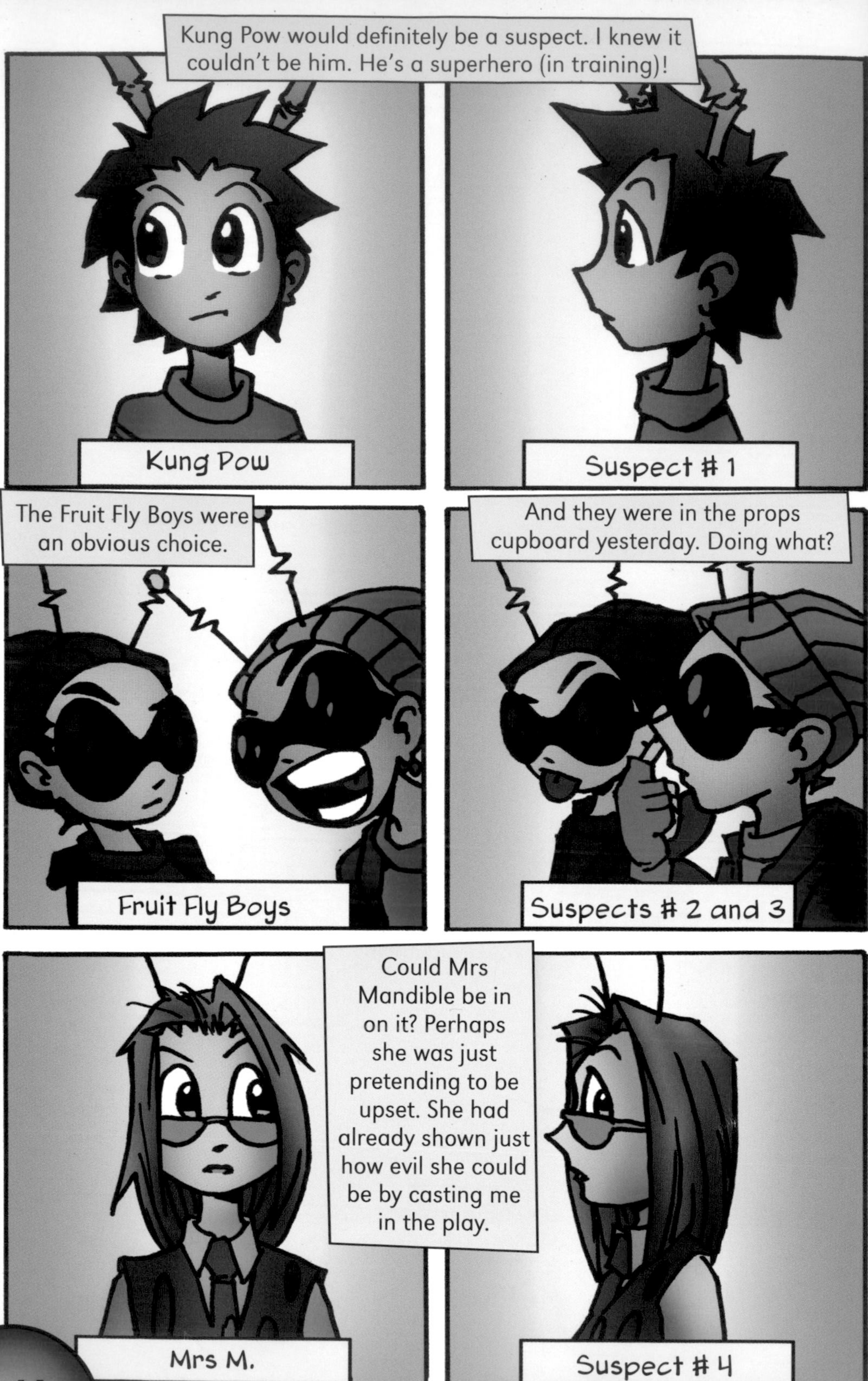

Kung Pow would definitely be a suspect. I knew it couldn't be him. He's a superhero (in training)!
Kung Pow
Suspect # 1
The Fruit Fly Boys were an obvious choice.
Fruit Fly Boys
And they were in the props cupboard yesterday. Doing what?
Suspects # 2 and 3
Could Mrs Mandible be in on it? Perhaps she was just pretending to be upset. She had already shown just how evil she could be by casting me in the play.
Mrs M.
Suspect # 4

Play time was my first chance to observe the Fruit Fly Boys.
Have you got it?
Yes, I've got it.
Here it is.
Well, let's see it.
Aha!
A copy of tomorrow's spelling test.
This time tomorrow, they'll be calling us the Spelling Bees.
SPELLING TEST ANSWERS
Spelling Bees. Good one.

Okay, it wasn't a painting. But it still stank worse than a dung beetle's nappy.
SWOOSH!
Hey!

Mrs Mandible was buzzing into the staff room when I caught up with her.
EADI
MATHS
MATHS
Turns out maths is good for something after all.

It's the perfect plan.
Hmmm?
No one will find out.
Oh really?
I'll keep it safely out of sight.
That's good enough for me.

HI YAHHHHHH!
WHAM!

Tiger Moth!
That's right!
I'm glad to see you!
No, you're not!
I've come up with the perfect plan to help you with your lines.
My lines?
Cue cards! We'll hide them at the front of the stage. No one will ever find out that you don't have all your lines memorized!
Cue cards. That's what you were talking about.
Exactly.

What about the painting?
Well, I'm horribly upset about it. I'm afraid Kung Pow is in big bug trouble. But the show must go on.
Must it?
And since we're using cue cards, now I can give you **more** lines! Isn't that wonderful?

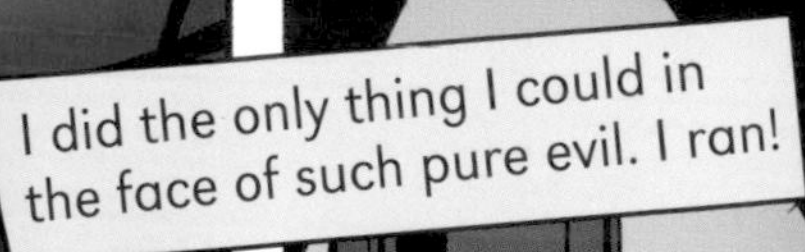
I did the only thing I could in the face of such pure evil. I ran!

Ten minutes until play practice. My ninja skills were failing me.
EXIT
I'm in so much trouble, Tiger!
I know.
Mrs Mandible's going to squash me like a fly!
I'm out of answers, Kung.

But my hyper ninja hearing kicked in.
I told you not to take it!
I know!
PROPS CUPBOARD
Listen! I knew something sinister was at work here!
Sounds like the Dragonfly gang.
PROPS CUPBOARD
Those rotten ankle-biters!
It's a really valuable painting!
How was I supposed to know that?
PROPS CUPBOARD
Or it's the Termite Twosome!
PROPS CUPBOARD
Those no-good bloodsuckers!

CUPBOARD
The props bug will get the blame!
Okay, apprentice. I've heard enough! Open the door.
Time for the "Roly-Poly Pow"?
Just like I taught you. We'll be on those bad bugs like maggots on meat.

POW!

HI YAHHHHH!
HI YAHHHHH!

I've caught you cold-handed!
Flutter ?! Sluggo ?!

What is going on here?!

We were putting it back! Honestly!
Here's your DeLacewing painting, Mrs Mandible.
And your culprits.
ME

Flutter? Sluggo? You took it?
We just borrowed it!
We wanted to practice the scene from Act Two, when Sluggo gives me the painting.
SLIME
We didn't know it was valuable!
Honest!

Allow me to dig deeper, Mrs Mandible. Shall I perform a ninja mind-swarm on them?
That won't be necessary this time. Well done, Tiger.
Sorry, Kung Pow.
The Missing DeLacewing Mystery was wrapped up tighter than a cockroach in a carpet.
And Kung Pow was in the clear. Thanks to Tiger Moth, Insect Ninja.

But my heightened ninja feelers still sensed evil close at hand.
Okay everyone, time for play rehearsal!
I knew it. Evil.

About the author

Aaron Reynolds loves insects and loves books, so Tiger Moth was a perfect blend of both. Aaron is the author of several great books for children, including *Chicks and Salsa*, which *Publishers Weekly* called "a literary fandango". Aaron had no idea what "fandango" meant. After looking it up in the dictionary, he learned the word means "playful and silly behaviour". Reynolds hopes to write several more fandangos in the future. He lives with his wife, two children, and four insect-obsessed cats.

About the illustrator

Erik Lervold was born in Puerto Rico, a small island in the Caribbean, and has been a professional painter. He attended the University of Puerto Rico's Mayaguez campus, where he studied Civil Engineering. Deciding that he wanted to be a full-time artist, he attended the Minneapolis College of Art and Design, studied Comic Art, and graduated in 2004. Erik teaches classes in libraries and has taught art in the Minnesota Children's Museum. He loves the colour green and has a collection of really big goggles. He also loves sandwiches. If you want him to be your friend, bring him a roast beef sandwich and he will love you forever.

Glossary

apprentice person learning skills from another person who already knows them

authenticity being real and not a fake or a copy. A painting has authenticity if it was painted by a real artist.

culprits people who are guilty

exoskeleton hard protective structure on the outside of the body (imagine your ribs on the outside!). Insects have exoskeletons.

hi yahhhh noise made when breaking down a door and surprising thieves

maggots early stage of an insect

ninja person trained in the ancient method of Japanese martial arts. Ninjas usually don't like acting in school plays.

parasite living thing that lives on or in another living thing, like fleas on a dog.

unsavoury something that has a bad taste or smell. Don't ever use the word "unsavoury" when you're eating dinner at a friend's house!

From the ninja notebook: undercover insects

Pest power!

The word ninja means "the art of stealth." Stealth is another word for "secret" or "undercover." Ninjas were masters of disguise and were experts at hiding and blending in with their surroundings. Lots of insects do the same thing. They hide or disguise themselves to keep from being eaten by larger creatures.

The Indian dead-leaf butterfly can hide in the open. Once the butterfly folds its wings, it looks like a dead leaf. No one would want to eat it for dinner!

The walking stick insect looks just like a twig or a small branch.

Small, yellow crab spiders sit on sunflowers where they blend in with the bright petals. When a bee zooms in to visit the flower, the hidden spider pounces. It catches the bee and drags it behind the flower to feast.

The caterpillar of the hawkmoth looks like a snake. This fake snake scares away any hungry birds that might be hunting for a tasty moth.

The carpenter moth has wings the colour of tree bark. When the insect rests on a tree, it opens its wings wide and seems to disappear against the tree trunk.

Discussion questions

1. Just as Tiger Moth had to be in the school play, sometimes you have to participate in something you don't want to do. What school activities don't you like and why? What are some ways to deal with an unpleasant activity?

2. If your friend was accused of stealing, but you knew that your friend was innocent, what would you do to help?

3. Kung Pow was almost blamed for stealing. Have you ever been blamed for something you didn't do? How did it make you feel and why?

Writing prompts

1. Imagine that you are a superhero. What would your name be? What would your superpower be? Like Tiger Moth, who would you save, and what would you save them from? When you're finished writing, try drawing your superhero.

2. Mrs Mandible has a painting that's special to her. What possession is special to you? How would you feel if it were lost or stolen?

More amazing adventures!

When Zack Allen is bullied at school, he invents a robot super suit to help him fight evil in the playground and beyond. He becomes Zinc Alloy, the world's newest superhero!